What Do You Know About Materials?

1   Draw and name two objects.

A _____	A _____

2a List three materials.

2b Describe the materials.

1 _____ is _____ .

2 _____ is _____ .

3 _____ is _____ .

Matching Materials

1 Draw and name something made from these materials.

A _____ made from plastic.	A _____ made from metal.
A _____ made from wood.	A _____ made from glass.

Identifying Materials

2. List four objects that can be made from wood.

   1 _____

   2 _____

   3 _____

   4 _____

3. Choose an object from your list that can be made from another material.

   What other material can it be made from?

   A _____ can also be made

   from _____ .

4. Wood is a natural material.
   Name another natural material.

   _____

5. Plastic is a manufactured material.
   Name two other manufactured materials.

   1 _____

   2 _____

Describing Toys

Look at these toys.

1. Match each toy to words that describe it. Draw lines to link the toy to all its properties.

Properties

Hard

Soft

Flexible (bendy)

Rough

Smooth

Toy Ducks

1. Choose two words to describe how each duck feels.

A — Toy duck for bath

B — Cuddly duck

I think duck A would feel _____

and _____.

I think duck B would feel _____

and _____.

2. How are the ducks similar? They are similar because

_____.

3. How are the ducks different? They are different because

_____.

Science Skills

Observe it!

Look closely at the diagrams of different materials. They show what the material looks like close up.

1 What are the materials?

Write the name of the material next to the diagram.

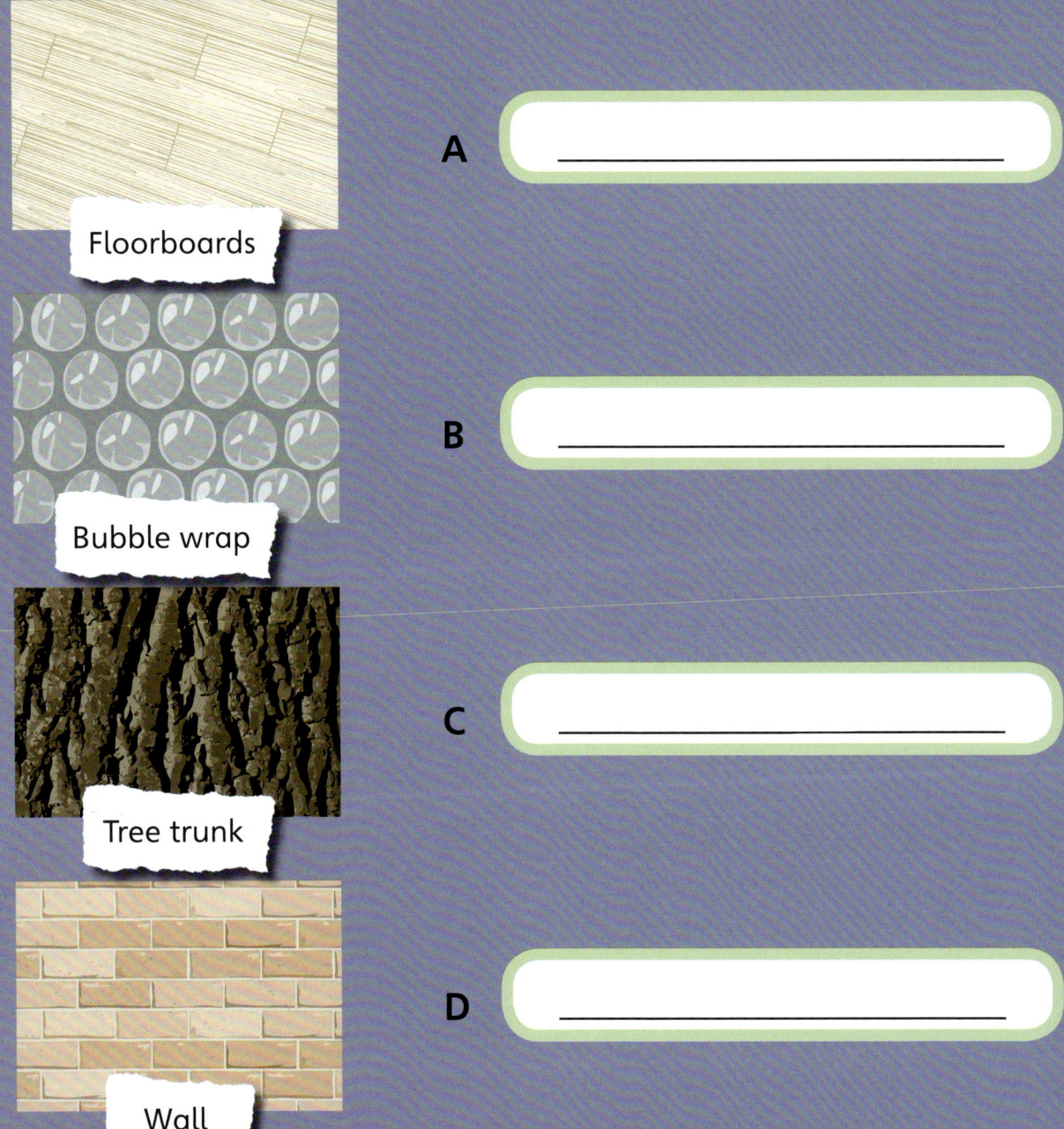

Identifying Materials

2 Draw a close-up picture of rock.

Rock is the name of the material and the object. Usually the object and the material are not same word.

3 Choose another material. Draw a close-up picture of it.

My material is _____

Identifying and Describing Liquids

1 List five different liquids.

1 _____

2 _____

3 _____

4 _____

5 _____

2 How would you identify water?

Write and draw pictures to describe water.

Water looks like this:

Words I would use to describe water:

_____

_____

Different Liquids

There are many different types of solids and liquids.

1. Look at these diagrams. Tick the ones that are liquids. The liquid might be inside a container.

Science Skills

Investigate it!

How runny are different liquids?

Choose three different liquids that are different thicknesses. My liquids are …

1 _____

2 _____

3 _____

1   Which liquid is the thickest? (1, 2 or 3)

_____

2   Which liquid is the thinnest? (1, 2 or 3)

_____

Gently pour the liquids from a spoon into a bowl.

3   Which liquid do you think will land in the bowl second?

_____

4   Why will it land second?

_____

_____

_____

Identifying Materials

5   Draw a picture of you doing the investigation.

6   What did you observe happen to the liquids?

_____

_____

Choosing Materials

Metal pan

1. Draw six objects. Write a suitable material under each one.

Identifying Materials

2. Complete the table with the six objects you have chosen. Write an *unsuitable* material next to each object in the table. The first one has been done for you.

Object	Unsuitable material
Pan	Chocolate

Choosing Materials

3 Why are the materials you have chosen unsuitable?

Object: unsuitable material	Why it is unsuitable
pan: chocolate	because it turns to liquid when it gets hot

Exploring Powders

1 List six solids that are found in very small pieces.

  1 _____

  2 _____

  3 _____

  4 _____

  5 _____

  6 _____

When the pieces are very, very small they are called powders.

2a Which of your six solids has the smallest pieces?

_____

2b Is it a powder?

_____

2c How is it used?

_____

Describing My Favourite Toy

1 Draw your favourite toy.
Label the materials it is made from.

My toy can be described as looking …

It feels …

2 What other materials could have been used to make your toy?

3 What materials would be *unsuitable* to make your toy?

16

INTERNATIONAL

Fuel curiosity, spark imagination.

| UK National Curriculum YEAR 1 | CAMBRIDGE primary Stages 1, 2 | Pearson iPRIMARY YEAR 1 |

Science Bug International is an exciting and comprehensive science programme that has been designed to make sure your children never stop asking questions about their world!

This Workbook contains questions from the Topic Book plus additional questions to reinforce and extend learning.

With full and comprehensive coverage of the skills and knowledge required for curriculum attainment, *Science Bug International* will help you to nurture and inspire your young scientist.

Series editor: Deborah Herridge
Author: Debbie Eccles

www.pearsonschools.co.uk
myorders@pearson.com

ISBN 978-0-435-19643-1